A GIFT FOR:

FROM:

Happy Mother's Day to our Wonderful, beautiful daughter-in-law.
all our love,
Ric + Gail

5-10-09

A Mother's Legacy
Copyright © 2006 Hallmark Licensing, Inc.

Published by Gift Books from Hallmark, a division of Hallmark Cards, Inc., under
license from J. Countryman®, a trademark of Thomas Nelson, Inc. Previous edition
copyright © 2000 J. Countryman, Inc.

Visit us on the Web at www.Hallmark.com.

All rights reserved. No part of this publication may be reproduced, transmitted,
or stored in any form or by any means without the prior written permission of
the publisher.

Editorial Director: Todd Hafer
Editor: Theresa Trinder
Art Director: Kevin Swanson
Designer: Michelle Nicolier
Production Artist: Dan Horton

BOK4326

ISBN: 978-1-59530-155-0

Printed and bound in China.

A MOTHER'S *Legacy*

Your Life Story in Your Own Words

GIFT BOOKS
from Hallmark

CONTENTS

Introduction

As the years go by, we become more and more aware of what's really important in life. With every passing season, we are reminded that the love and traditions a family shares are treasures beyond value.

Lying within our memories are the personal stories behind those treasures. This book is intended to help you recall and reflect upon those memories and to share them with the ones you love. Open-ended questions will ask you to think about your childhood, special relationships, cherished traditions, personal triumphs and failures, sad partings and joyous reunions—all the events big and small that have helped you to become the person you are today.

As you think about the questions in this book, don't be intimidated to put your thoughts and memories on paper. Writing is an exercise of discovery. You may recall a particular sight or sound from your childhood. You may remember something you thought you had forgotten. Maybe you will see a past event from a different perspective. You have much to share—and you may find that you learn something about yourself in the process.

How you choose to complete this book is up to you. You may follow it from beginning to end or in random order. You might complete your journaling in one week or over the course of several years. Whatever method you choose, one thing is certain: the memories and messages you record here will be a gift beyond value. May this gift draw you closer to your family as you share it, and may your family enjoy the words and wonder it holds for years to come.

Personal Portrait

CELEBRATE THE WOMAN YOU ARE...
THE GIFT YOU ARE TO THE WORLD.

Personal Portrait

What is the date and place of your birth?

_____

What is your full given name?

_____

_____

Who selected your name?

_____

Why were you given this name?

_____

_____

_____

_____

Do you have a nickname or did you have one as a child?
How did you get it?

_____

_____

_____

_____

_____

_____

_____

_____

What is your mother's full name and the date and place
of her birth?

_____

_____

_____

What is your father's full name and date and place of
his birth?

_____

_____

_____

What are the names of your siblings and the dates and
places of their births?

_____

_____

_____

_____

_____

_____

_____

_____

_____

Personal Portrait

What are the names of your maternal grandparents;
the dates and places of their births?

_____

_____

_____

_____

_____

_____

_____

_____

What are the names of your paternal grandparents;
the dates and places of their births?

_____

_____

_____

_____

_____

_____

_____

_____

_____

What is your husband's full given name;
the date and place of his birth?

_____

_____

_____

_____

What are the names of your children;
the dates and places of their births?

_____

_____

_____

_____

_____

_____

_____

_____

_____

_____

_____

_____

_____

Personal Portrait

....

What are the names of your grandchildren?

Great-grandchildren?

What are the dates and places of their births?

_____

_____

_____

_____

_____

_____

_____

_____

_____

_____

_____

_____

_____

_____

_____

_____

_____

_____

_____

What is your favorite way to spend your free time?

_____

_____

_____

_____

_____

_____

_____

_____

_____

_____

_____

_____

_____

_____

_____

_____

_____

_____

Personal Portrait

....

Do you have a favorite song?

Why is this song special to you?

_____

_____

_____

_____

_____

_____

_____

_____

Do you have a favorite book?

Why does it appeal to you?

_____

_____

_____

_____

_____

_____

_____

_____

Is there a television show you most enjoy?

Why is it a favorite?

_____

_____

_____

_____

_____

_____

_____

_____

Is there a movie you have watched again and again?

Why is it so special to you?

_____

_____

_____

_____

_____

_____

_____

_____

Personal Portrait

Do you have a favorite food or meal?

_____

_____

_____

_____

_____

A favorite outfit or article of clothing?

_____

_____

_____

_____

_____

A favorite sport or sports team?

_____

_____

_____

_____

_____

What are your special gifts or talents?

How have you used them throughout your life?

_____

_____

_____

_____

_____

_____

_____

_____

_____

_____

_____

_____

_____

_____

_____

_____

_____

_____

_____

_____

Personal Portrait

What is one of your best characteristics?

_____

_____

_____

_____

_____

_____

_____

_____

_____

Is there a characteristic you wish you could change
about yourself?

_____

_____

_____

_____

_____

_____

_____

_____

Describe a typical day in your life right now.

_____

_____

_____

_____

_____

_____

_____

_____

_____

_____

_____

_____

_____

_____

_____

_____

_____

_____

_____

_____

_____

Childhood

THE WORLD IS FILLED WITH WONDER
WHEN YOU SEE IT THROUGH
THE EYES OF A CHILD.

Childhood

Describe your childhood home.

_____

_____

_____

_____

_____

_____

_____

_____

_____

Describe your childhood bedroom.

Did you share it with anyone?

_____

_____

_____

_____

_____

_____

_____

_____

Describe the neighborhood you grew up in.

_____

_____

_____

_____

_____

_____

_____

_____

_____

_____

_____

_____

_____

_____

_____

_____

_____

_____

Childhood

What were your chores and responsibilities?

_____

_____

_____

_____

_____

_____

_____

_____

_____

_____

_____

_____

_____

Did you get an allowance?

How much was it?

_____

_____

_____

_____

_____

Did you spend more of your free time indoors or outdoors?

_____

_____

_____

_____

_____

What was your favorite outdoor activity?

_____

_____

_____

_____

What indoor activity did you enjoy most?

_____

_____

_____

_____

_____

Childhood

Did you have any special interests or talents as a child?
Did you take lessons of any kind?

_____

_____

_____

_____

_____

_____

_____

_____

_____

_____

_____

Was there something you always wanted to try and never
got the chance?

_____

_____

_____

_____

_____

_____

Do you remember a favorite toy?

_____

_____

_____

_____

Did you have a favorite book or story?

_____

_____

_____

_____

Did you ever have a hideaway, clubhouse, or other special place that was "yours"?

_____

_____

_____

_____

_____

_____

_____

Childhood

Which friends from your childhood do you most remember?
What is memorable about these friends?

_____

_____

_____

_____

_____

_____

_____

_____

What did you and your friends do for fun?

_____

_____

_____

_____

_____

_____

_____

_____

_____

Were you part of a club, troop, or other organization?

What do you remember about your group?

_____

_____

_____

_____

_____

_____

_____

_____

_____

Did you attend religious services as a girl?

What are your memories of this experience?

_____

_____

_____

_____

_____

_____

_____

_____

_____

Childhood

Record one or two of your most treasured
childhood memories.

_____

_____

_____

_____

_____

_____

_____

_____

_____

_____

Is there a scent or sound that immediately takes you back
to childhood?

Why? What does it bring to mind?

_____

_____

_____

What are some of the childhood experiences that helped
you to become the woman you are today?

_____

_____

_____

_____

_____

_____

_____

_____

_____

_____

_____

_____

_____

_____

_____

_____

_____

_____

_____

Family Life

A FAMILY IS A CIRCLE OF LOVE...
FORMED BY MEMORIES,
FILLED WITH DEVOTION.

Family Life

What was your mother like when you were young?

Her appearance? Her manner?

_____

_____

_____

_____

_____

_____

_____

_____

_____

_____

_____

_____

_____

How would you finish this sentence?

"One thing my mom always said was..."

_____

_____

_____

_____

What was your mother's daily life like?

Did she work outside the home? How did her work affect you?

_____

_____

_____

_____

_____

_____

_____

_____

_____

_____

_____

_____

_____

_____

_____

_____

_____

_____

Family Life

What did you most enjoy doing with your mother?

_____

_____

_____

_____

_____

What is a favorite memory of your mother?

Why this memory?

_____

_____

_____

_____

_____

_____

_____

_____

_____

_____

_____

_____

_____

_____

What was your mother's attitude toward life?

How did her attitude affect you?

_____

_____

_____

_____

_____

_____

_____

_____

_____

_____

_____

_____

_____

_____

_____

_____

_____

_____

_____

_____

Family Life

In what ways are you like your mother?

_____

_____

_____

_____

_____

_____

_____

_____

_____

In what ways are you different?

_____

_____

_____

_____

_____

_____

_____

_____

_____

What was your father like when you were young?

His appearance and manner?

_____

_____

_____

_____

_____

_____

_____

_____

_____

_____

_____

How would you finish this sentence?

"One thing my dad always said was..."

_____

_____

_____

Family Life

What was your father's daily life like?

What did he do for a living? How did his work affect you?

_____

_____

_____

_____

_____

_____

_____

_____

_____

_____

_____

_____

_____

_____

_____

_____

_____

_____

_____

_____

_____

What did you most enjoy doing with your father?

_____

_____

_____

_____

_____

What is a favorite memory of your father?

Why this memory?

_____

_____

_____

_____

_____

_____

_____

_____

_____

_____

_____

_____

_____

_____

_____

_____

Family Life

What was your father's attitude toward life?

How did his attitude affect you?

_____

_____

_____

_____

_____

_____

_____

_____

_____

_____

_____

_____

_____

_____

_____

_____

_____

_____

_____

How are you like your father?

_____

_____

_____

_____

_____

_____

_____

_____

_____

How are you different?

_____

_____

_____

_____

_____

_____

_____

_____

_____

Family Life

If you have siblings, record any special memories that you have of each of them.

_____

_____

_____

_____

_____

_____

_____

_____

_____

_____

_____

_____

_____

_____

_____

_____

_____

_____

_____

_____

How did you and your siblings get along?

_____

_____

_____

_____

_____

_____

_____

_____

Describe a time when you were grateful to have a brother
or sister.

_____

_____

_____

_____

_____

_____

_____

_____

_____

Family Life

Describe your role in your immediate family.

Did you have any unique traits or special responsibilities?

_____

_____

_____

_____

_____

_____

_____

_____

_____

_____

_____

_____

_____

_____

_____

_____

_____

_____

_____

_____

What talents, abilities, or qualities did your parents
nurture in you?

_____

_____

_____

_____

_____

_____

_____

_____

What kind of person did your parents encourage you to be?

_____

_____

_____

_____

_____

_____

_____

_____

Family Life

What were your family's circumstances when you were growing up? *How did they affect you?*

_____

_____

_____

_____

_____

_____

_____

_____

_____

_____

_____

_____

_____

_____

_____

_____

_____

_____

_____

_____

_____

Did your family have any pets?

Did you have a favorite pet?

_____

_____

_____

_____

_____

_____

_____

_____

Did you enjoy having a pet?

Why or why not?

_____

_____

_____

_____

_____

_____

_____

_____

_____

_____

Family Life

What did your family most enjoy doing together?

_____

_____

_____

_____

_____

_____

_____

_____

_____

_____

_____

_____

_____

_____

_____

_____

_____

_____

_____

_____

What are your early memories of your grandparents?

_____

_____

_____

_____

_____

_____

_____

_____

_____

_____

_____

_____

_____

_____

_____

_____

_____

_____

_____

_____

Family Life

What kind of work did they do?

_____

_____

_____

_____

_____

_____

_____

_____

_____

Where did they live?

Describe their home.

_____

_____

_____

_____

_____

_____

_____

_____

_____

_____

What do you remember most about spending time with
your grandparents?

_____

_____

_____

_____

_____

_____

_____

_____

What is one valuable lesson you learned from a grandmother
or grandfather?

_____

_____

_____

_____

_____

_____

_____

_____

Family Life

What memories or knowledge do you have of your
great-grandparents?

_____

_____

_____

_____

What do you know about your family history?

Where are your ancestors from? Do you feel connected to this heritage?

_____

_____

_____

_____

_____

_____

_____

_____

_____

_____

_____

_____

_____

_____

Describe a significant memory of an aunt or uncle.

_____

_____

_____

_____

_____

_____

_____

_____

_____

Describe a favorite memory of your cousins or family friends.

_____

_____

_____

_____

_____

_____

_____

_____

_____

Family Life

Did you attend family reunions?

What were these events like? What did you enjoy about them?

_____

_____

_____

_____

_____

_____

_____

_____

_____

_____

_____

_____

_____

_____

_____

_____

_____

_____

_____

Describe dinnertime with your family.

Who cooked? Where did you eat? What did you talk about?

_____

_____

_____

_____

_____

_____

_____

_____

_____

_____

_____

_____

_____

_____

_____

_____

_____

_____

_____

Family Life

What was your favorite home-cooked meal?

_____

_____

_____

_____

_____

_____

_____

_____

_____

_____

_____

_____

Did your family eat out?

Did you have a favorite place to go?

_____

_____

_____

_____

_____

What were weekends like when you were a child?

_____

_____

_____

_____

_____

_____

_____

_____

_____

_____

_____

_____

_____

_____

_____

_____

_____

_____

_____

Family Life

Describe a memorable family outing or vacation.

Where did you go? What did you do?

_____

_____

_____

_____

_____

_____

_____

_____

_____

_____

_____

_____

_____

_____

_____

_____

_____

_____

_____

How did your family life then influence your family life now?

_____

_____

_____

_____

_____

_____

_____

_____

_____

_____

_____

_____

_____

_____

_____

_____

_____

_____

_____

_____

Education

LIVE. LOVE. LEARN.

Education

Where did you attend elementary school?

How did you travel between school and home?

_____

_____

_____

_____

_____

_____

What are your earliest memories of attending school?

_____

_____

_____

_____

_____

_____

_____

_____

_____

_____

_____

What did you enjoy most about elementary school?

_____

_____

_____

_____

_____

_____

_____

_____

_____

What did you least enjoy?

_____

_____

_____

_____

_____

_____

_____

_____

Education

....

Where did you attend middle school?

_____

_____

_____

_____

Where did you attend high school?

_____

_____

_____

_____

What did you most enjoy about middle school and
high school?

_____

_____

_____

_____

_____

_____

_____

_____

_____

_____

What extracurricular activities did you participate in?

Why did you choose these activities? Did you have a favorite?

_____

_____

_____

_____

_____

_____

_____

_____

Did you have a special role or responsibility in any of these activities?

_____

_____

_____

_____

_____

_____

_____

_____

Education

Who were your favorite teachers?

What influence did they have on you?

_____

_____

_____

_____

_____

_____

_____

_____

_____

_____

_____

_____

_____

_____

_____

_____

_____

_____

What were the fashion trends from your school days?

Did you follow them? Why or why not?

_____

_____

_____

_____

_____

_____

_____

_____

_____

_____

_____

_____

_____

_____

_____

_____

_____

_____

_____

Education

What songs were most popular when you were in high school?

_____
_____
_____
_____
_____
_____

Did you have favorite movies from this time?

_____
_____
_____
_____
_____

Did you have a favorite TV show that you watched regularly?

_____
_____
_____
_____
_____
_____

When did you learn to drive?

Who taught you?

_____

_____

_____

_____

_____

_____

_____

Did you have your own car?

What kind was it? How did you feel about it at the time?

_____

_____

_____

_____

_____

_____

_____

_____

_____

Education

What did you do for entertainment?

Parties, dances, concerts, movies?

_____

_____

_____

_____

_____

_____

_____

_____

_____

_____

_____

_____

_____

_____

_____

_____

_____

_____

_____

_____

Who were your best friends from high school?

Share a vivid memory or a funny story.

_____

_____

_____

_____

_____

_____

_____

_____

_____

_____

_____

_____

_____

_____

_____

_____

_____

_____

_____

_____

Education

Describe any challenges you may have faced during your
middle school and high school years.

_____

_____

_____

_____

_____

_____

_____

_____

_____

_____

_____

_____

_____

_____

_____

_____

_____

_____

_____

What are you glad to have done during your middle school and high school years?

_____

_____

_____

_____

_____

_____

_____

_____

_____

_____

_____

_____

_____

_____

_____

_____

_____

_____

Education

What were your goals and aspirations after high school?
How did these change with time?

_____

_____

_____

_____

_____

_____

_____

_____

_____

_____

_____

_____

_____

_____

_____

_____

_____

_____

_____

_____

What path did you choose after high school?

_____

_____

_____

_____

_____

_____

_____

_____

_____

_____

_____

_____

Did you continue your studies?

Where? In what field?

_____

_____

_____

_____

Education

....

Did you move away from home?

If so, describe your experience.

_____

_____

_____

_____

_____

_____

_____

_____

_____

What was your first place like?

_____

_____

_____

_____

_____

_____

_____

_____

_____

_____

What are some of your favorite memories from this time?

_____

_____

_____

_____

_____

_____

_____

_____

_____

_____

_____

_____

_____

_____

_____

_____

_____

_____

_____

Work

THE WORKING MOM...

IS THERE ANY OTHER KIND?

Work

What did you want to do when you grew up?

_____

_____

_____

_____

_____

_____

_____

_____

_____

What was your first job?

How did you get it? What did it pay?

_____

_____

_____

_____

_____

_____

_____

_____

_____

_____

How did you feel when you first began working?

_____

_____

_____

_____

_____

_____

_____

_____

What led you to your line of work?

_____

_____

_____

_____

_____

_____

_____

_____

_____

Work

....

What have you enjoyed about your work?

_____

_____

_____

_____

_____

_____

_____

_____

Have there been any particular challenges?

_____

_____

_____

_____

_____

_____

_____

_____

What was the worst job you ever had?

_____

_____

_____

_____

_____

_____

_____

_____

_____

What was the most enjoyable or rewarding job you ever had?

_____

_____

_____

_____

_____

_____

_____

_____

_____

Work

Has a career or job change ever required you to move?

Where did you go and how did you feel about it?

_____

_____

_____

_____

_____

_____

_____

_____

_____

_____

_____

Have any of your jobs involved travel?

Describe a memorable trip.

_____

_____

_____

_____

Has anyone ever acted as a mentor to you?

What did you learn from that person?

_____

_____

_____

_____

_____

_____

_____

_____

_____

_____

_____

_____

_____

_____

_____

_____

_____

_____

Work

What special friends have you made as a result of your work?

_____

_____

_____

_____

_____

_____

_____

_____

Is there one person in particular you are most grateful to
have met? *Why?*

_____

_____

_____

_____

_____

_____

_____

_____

_____

How much of your time is devoted to work at home?

_____

_____

_____

_____

_____

_____

_____

_____

Do you find this type of work rewarding?

Why or why not?

_____

_____

_____

_____

_____

_____

_____

_____

_____

Love and Marriage

IS THERE ANY GREATER JOY
THAN TO BE IN LOVE?

Love and Marriage

Who was your first crush?

_____

_____

_____

_____

When did you attend your first boy/girl party?

_____

_____

_____

_____

What do you remember about your first kiss?

_____

_____

_____

_____

_____

_____

_____

_____

What do you remember about your first date?

_____

_____

_____

_____

_____

_____

_____

_____

_____

What was a typical date like at that time?

_____

_____

_____

_____

_____

_____

_____

_____

Love and Marriage

Who was your first love?

What did you learn from this relationship?

_____

_____

_____

_____

_____

_____

_____

_____

_____

_____

_____

_____

_____

_____

_____

_____

_____

_____

_____

_____

How old were you when you met your husband?

_____

_____

How did you meet?

_____

_____

_____

_____

_____

_____

_____

_____

_____

_____

_____

_____

_____

_____

_____

_____

_____

Love and Marriage

What attracted you to him?

_____

_____

_____

_____

_____

What was your first impression of him?

Did this impression change with time?

_____

_____

_____

_____

_____

_____

_____

_____

_____

_____

_____

_____

What did you enjoy doing together?

_____

_____

_____

_____

_____

_____

_____

_____

Share a memory from when you were dating.

_____

_____

_____

_____

_____

_____

_____

_____

Love and Marriage

....

When did you know that he was "the one"?

How did you know?

_____

_____

_____

_____

_____

_____

_____

_____

_____

_____

_____

_____

_____

_____

_____

_____

_____

_____

Describe the marriage proposal.

Who proposed and how?

_____

_____

_____

_____

_____

_____

_____

_____

_____

_____

_____

_____

_____

_____

_____

_____

_____

_____

_____

_____

Love and Marriage

Where and when were you married?

_____

_____

_____

What did you wear?

_____

_____

_____

_____

_____

_____

_____

What did he wear?

_____

_____

_____

_____

_____

Did you have a maid of honor and a best man?

Who did you choose and why?

_____

_____

_____

_____

_____

_____

_____

_____

_____

_____

Did you have a wedding song?

Why did you choose this song?

_____

_____

_____

_____

_____

Love and Marriage

What is your most cherished memory from your wedding day?

_____

_____

_____

_____

_____

_____

_____

_____

_____

_____

_____

_____

_____

_____

_____

_____

_____

_____

_____

_____

Where did you go on your honeymoon?

Recall a special moment or event from your trip.

_____

_____

_____

_____

_____

_____

_____

_____

_____

_____

_____

_____

_____

_____

_____

_____

_____

_____

_____

_____

Love and Marriage

Where did you live after you got married?

What do you remember about this place?

_____

_____

_____

_____

_____

_____

_____

_____

_____

_____

_____

_____

_____

_____

_____

_____

_____

_____

_____

Describe a typical evening during the first years of
your marriage.

_____

_____

_____

_____

_____

_____

_____

_____

_____

_____

_____

_____

_____

_____

_____

_____

_____

_____

Love and Marriage

When did you start thinking about having children?

What about having children did you look forward to?

_____

_____

_____

_____

_____

_____

_____

_____

_____

_____

_____

_____

_____

_____

_____

_____

_____

_____

_____

_____

_____

Who were some of your closest friends when you were
first married?

What did you enjoy doing together?

_____

_____

_____

_____

_____

_____

_____

_____

_____

_____

_____

_____

_____

_____

_____

_____

Love and Marriage

What activities have you and your husband enjoyed together?

_____

_____

_____

_____

_____

_____

_____

_____

_____

_____

_____

_____

_____

_____

_____

_____

_____

_____

_____

_____

_____

What have you found most rewarding about marriage?

_____

_____

_____

_____

_____

_____

_____

_____

_____

_____

_____

_____

_____

_____

_____

_____

_____

_____

Love and Marriage

....

What do you think is most important in maintaining a
healthy marriage?

_____

_____

_____

_____

_____

_____

_____

_____

_____

_____

_____

_____

_____

_____

_____

_____

_____

_____

Has there been an event in your marriage when sharing
and partnership were particularly important?

_____

_____

_____

_____

_____

_____

_____

_____

_____

_____

_____

_____

_____

_____

_____

_____

_____

_____

_____

Motherhood

YOU NEVER OUTGROW YOUR MOTHER'S LOVE.

Motherhood

How did you feel when you first learned that you were
going to become a mother?

_____

_____

_____

_____

_____

_____

_____

_____

_____

How did you share the news with friends and relatives?

_____

_____

_____

_____

_____

_____

_____

_____

Describe your feelings on the day your first child was born.

_____

_____

_____

_____

_____

_____

_____

_____

_____

_____

_____

_____

_____

_____

_____

_____

_____

_____

Motherhood

....

How did becoming a mother change your life?

Was motherhood different from what you had expected?

_____

_____

_____

_____

_____

_____

_____

_____

_____

_____

_____

_____

_____

_____

_____

_____

_____

_____

_____

_____

_____

_____

How did you choose your children's names?

Do they have a special meaning?

_____

_____

_____

_____

_____

_____

_____

_____

_____

_____

_____

_____

_____

_____

_____

_____

_____

_____

Motherhood

....

What are your most vivid memories of your children's
early years?

_____

_____

_____

_____

_____

_____

_____

_____

_____

_____

_____

_____

_____

_____

_____

_____

_____

_____

_____

_____

What activities did you most enjoy with your children when they were young?

_____

_____

_____

_____

_____

_____

_____

_____

_____

_____

_____

_____

_____

_____

_____

_____

_____

_____

_____

Motherhood

....

How did you find time to yourself?

_____

_____

_____

_____

_____

_____

_____

_____

_____

_____

_____

_____

What did you do for child-free entertainment?

_____

_____

_____

_____

_____

_____

_____

What similarities do you see between yourself and
your children?

_____

_____

_____

_____

_____

_____

_____

_____

What similarities do you see among your children?

_____

_____

_____

_____

_____

_____

_____

_____

Motherhood

What values did you try to nurture in your children?

_____

_____

_____

_____

_____

_____

_____

_____

_____

_____

_____

_____

_____

_____

_____

_____

_____

_____

_____

_____

What has been your greatest joy in being a mother?

_____

_____

_____

_____

_____

_____

_____

_____

_____

What has been the greatest challenge?

_____

_____

_____

_____

_____

_____

_____

_____

_____

Motherhood

How does your children's upbringing compare to your own?

_____

_____

_____

_____

_____

_____

_____

_____

_____

_____

_____

_____

_____

_____

_____

_____

_____

_____

_____

_____

Is there anything you know now that you wish you'd known when you first became a mother?

_____

_____

_____

_____

_____

_____

_____

_____

_____

_____

_____

_____

_____

_____

_____

_____

_____

_____

_____

_____

Motherhood

What is the most important thing you've learned from being a mother?

_____

_____

_____

_____

_____

_____

_____

_____

_____

_____

_____

_____

_____

_____

_____

_____

_____

_____

_____

What are the things you hope your children have learned from you?

_____

_____

_____

_____

_____

_____

_____

_____

_____

_____

_____

_____

_____

_____

_____

_____

_____

Celebrations

MAY EVERY CELEBRATION
BE FILLED WITH HAPPINESS
AND WARMED BY THE LOVE
OF FAMILY AND FRIENDS.

Celebrations

How did your family celebrate special occasions when you were a child?

With parties, family, and friends? Quietly at home?

_____

_____

_____

_____

_____

_____

_____

_____

_____

_____

_____

_____

_____

_____

_____

_____

_____

_____

How was your birthday celebrated when you were young?

_____

_____

_____

_____

_____

_____

_____

_____

What is your fondest birthday memory?

_____

_____

_____

_____

_____

_____

_____

_____

Celebrations

....

How did you celebrate your children's birthdays when they
were young?

_____

_____

_____

_____

_____

_____

_____

_____

_____

_____

_____

_____

_____

_____

_____

_____

_____

_____

_____

Describe an especially memorable birthday celebration.

Why was it so special?

_____

_____

_____

_____

_____

_____

_____

_____

_____

_____

_____

_____

_____

_____

_____

_____

_____

_____

_____

Celebrations

Describe an especially memorable gift you received.

Who was it from?

_____

_____

_____

_____

_____

_____

_____

_____

Describe an especially memorable gift you gave.

Who was it for?

_____

_____

_____

_____

_____

_____

_____

_____

What holiday celebrations from your childhood stand out most in your memory?

_____

_____

_____

_____

_____

_____

_____

_____

_____

_____

_____

_____

_____

_____

_____

_____

_____

_____

_____

Celebrations

What was the first holiday gathering you hosted?

Was it successful?

_____

_____

_____

_____

_____

_____

_____

_____

Have you enjoyed hosting parties?

Why or why not?

_____

_____

_____

_____

_____

_____

_____

What holidays has your family most enjoyed celebrating?

_____

_____

_____

_____

_____

_____

_____

_____

_____

_____

_____

_____

_____

_____

_____

_____

_____

_____

Celebrations

What has been the most meaningful holiday for you
as a parent?

_____

_____

_____

_____

_____

_____

_____

_____

_____

_____

_____

_____

_____

_____

_____

_____

_____

_____

_____

_____

What holiday traditions from your childhood did you pass on to your children?

What are the origins of those traditions?

_____

_____

_____

_____

_____

_____

_____

_____

_____

_____

_____

_____

_____

_____

_____

_____

_____

_____

Celebrations

....

Did you begin any new traditions with your children?

_____

_____

_____

_____

_____

_____

_____

_____

_____

_____

_____

_____

_____

_____

_____

_____

_____

_____

_____

Please share a cherished memory from a family
holiday celebration.

_____

_____

_____

_____

_____

_____

_____

_____

_____

_____

_____

_____

_____

_____

_____

_____

_____

_____

_____

_____

Life Events

MOMENT BY MOMENT, DAY BY DAY,
FAMILIES CREATE A LIFETIME OF MEMORIES.

Life Events

....

What was the happiest time of your life?

_____

_____

_____

_____

_____

_____

_____

_____

_____

What was the saddest?

_____

_____

_____

_____

_____

_____

_____

_____

_____

What was the busiest time of your life?

_____

_____

_____

_____

_____

_____

_____

_____

_____

What was the most relaxed?

_____

_____

_____

_____

_____

_____

_____

_____

_____

Life Events

Is there an event in your life that has changed you in some way?

_____

_____

_____

_____

_____

_____

_____

_____

_____

_____

_____

_____

_____

_____

_____

_____

_____

_____

_____

Have you ever been in an accident, had major surgery,
or suffered a similar challenge?
If so, how did it affect you?

_____

_____

_____

_____

_____

_____

_____

_____

_____

_____

_____

_____

_____

_____

_____

_____

_____

_____

_____

_____

Life Events

Did tragedy ever strike you or a loved one?

How did you respond? How did your family and friends respond?

_____

_____

_____

_____

_____

_____

_____

_____

_____

_____

_____

_____

_____

_____

_____

_____

_____

_____

_____

What was the most difficult decision you had to make in your life?

Would you make the same decision again?

_____

_____

_____

_____

_____

_____

_____

_____

_____

_____

_____

_____

_____

_____

_____

_____

_____

Life Events

Do you enjoy travel? Why or why not?

Who are your favorite travel partners?

_____

_____

_____

_____

_____

_____

_____

_____

_____

_____

_____

_____

_____

_____

_____

_____

_____

_____

_____

What is the most fun, interesting, or exciting place you've ever visited?

_____

_____

_____

_____

_____

_____

_____

_____

_____

_____

_____

_____

_____

_____

_____

_____

_____

_____

_____

Life Events

Have you ever helped someone in need?

If so, how?

_____

_____

_____

_____

_____

_____

_____

_____

_____

_____

_____

_____

_____

_____

_____

_____

_____

_____

_____

_____

_____

Have you ever dedicated yourself to a cause or organization?

Why was it important to you?

_____

_____

_____

_____

_____

_____

_____

_____

_____

_____

_____

_____

_____

_____

_____

_____

_____

_____

_____

Life Events

....

Did you ever play on a team or participate in another
competitive activity?
How did you benefit from it?

_____

_____

_____

Have you ever received an award or other type of recognition?
If so, what for? How did receiving it make you feel?

_____

_____

_____

_____

_____

_____

_____

_____

_____

_____

_____

_____

_____

_____

_____

_____

_____

_____

_____

Life Events

What have you done in your life that you are especially proud of?

_____

_____

_____

_____

_____

_____

_____

_____

_____

_____

_____

_____

_____

_____

_____

_____

_____

_____

_____

What do you regard as the most important invention or
discovery in your lifetime?

How did it affect the way you live?

_____

_____

_____

_____

_____

_____

_____

_____

_____

_____

_____

_____

_____

_____

_____

_____

_____

Life Events

....

What do you see as the most important political or cultural

events of your lifetime?

How did they affect you?

_____

_____

_____

_____

_____

_____

_____

_____

_____

_____

_____

_____

_____

_____

_____

_____

_____

_____

_____

In what ways has society changed since your youth?

_____

_____

_____

_____

_____

_____

_____

_____

_____

_____

_____

_____

_____

_____

_____

_____

_____

_____

Life Events

....

What is one thing you would never change about the way
you've lived your life?

_____

_____

_____

_____

_____

_____

_____

_____

_____

_____

_____

_____

_____

_____

_____

_____

_____

_____

_____

_____

_____

What is one thing you wish you had done differently?

_____

_____

_____

_____

_____

_____

_____

_____

_____

_____

_____

_____

_____

_____

_____

_____

_____

Life Events

What are your hopes for national or world events in the next ten years?

_____

_____

_____

_____

_____

_____

_____

_____

_____

_____

_____

_____

_____

_____

_____

_____

_____

_____

_____

_____

_____

What are your hopes for yourself and your family in the next ten years?

_____

_____

_____

_____

_____

_____

_____

_____

_____

_____

_____

_____

_____

_____

_____

_____

_____

_____

Inspiration

IT IS A MIRACLE HOW A LIFE
CAN BE TOUCHED SO DEEPLY
BY ONE CARING GESTURE,
ONE SMALL KINDNESS AT A TIME.

Inspiration

Who were your role models when you were young?
What did you learn from them?

_____

_____

_____

_____

_____

_____

_____

_____

_____

_____

_____

_____

_____

_____

_____

_____

_____

_____

_____

What valuable advice did you receive from an adult when you were young?

What were the circumstances?

_____

_____

_____

_____

_____

_____

_____

_____

_____

_____

_____

_____

_____

_____

_____

_____

_____

Inspiration

Who have you consulted most often for guidance over
the years?

_____

_____

_____

_____

_____

_____

_____

_____

Who do you turn to now for advice?

_____

_____

_____

_____

_____

_____

_____

_____

_____

Who has made the greatest impact on your life?

_____

_____

_____

_____

_____

_____

_____

_____

_____

_____

_____

_____

_____

_____

_____

_____

_____

_____

_____

Inspiration

....

What role does religion or spirituality play in your life?
Has this changed over the years?

_____

_____

_____

_____

_____

_____

_____

_____

_____

_____

_____

_____

_____

_____

_____

_____

_____

_____

_____

Is there a certain place that you go to for comfort or to unwind?

Why is this place meaningful?

_____

_____

_____

_____

_____

_____

_____

_____

_____

_____

_____

_____

_____

_____

_____

_____

_____

_____

_____

Inspiration

What is your most treasured possession?

Why is it so valuable?

_____

_____

_____

_____

_____

_____

_____

_____

_____

_____

_____

_____

_____

_____

_____

_____

_____

_____

_____

_____

If you could keep only one family photo, which would it be?
Why is it special?

_____

_____

_____

_____

_____

_____

_____

_____

_____

_____

_____

_____

_____

_____

_____

_____

_____

_____

Inspiration

What in your life are you most thankful for?

_____

_____

_____

_____

_____

_____

_____

_____

_____

_____

_____

_____

_____

_____

_____

_____

_____

_____

_____

_____

What in your life gives you the greatest sense of pride?

Inspiration

....

Is there a celebrity or political figure for whom you have
a special respect?

What makes this person admirable?

_____

_____

_____

_____

_____

_____

_____

_____

_____

_____

_____

_____

_____

_____

_____

_____

_____

Have you ever attended a speech, recital, or concert that had a great effect on you?

If not, who would you like to see and why?

_____

_____

_____

_____

_____

_____

_____

_____

_____

_____

_____

_____

_____

_____

_____

_____

_____

_____

_____

Inspiration

....

Is there a book that has influenced you in a significant way?
How and why did it affect you?

_____

_____

_____

_____

_____

_____

_____

_____

_____

_____

_____

_____

_____

_____

_____

_____

_____

_____

_____

_____

_____

Is there a poem, passage, or quote that you will always remember?

What does it mean to you?

_____

_____

_____

_____

_____

_____

_____

_____

_____

_____

_____

_____

_____

_____

_____

_____

_____

_____

_____

Inspiration

Is there a time you depended on someone else for help?

_____

_____

_____

_____

_____

_____

_____

_____

_____

_____

_____

_____

_____

_____

_____

_____

_____

_____

_____

_____

How would you describe success?

_____

_____

_____

_____

_____

_____

_____

_____

What do you feel is one way to achieve it?

_____

_____

_____

_____

_____

_____

_____

_____

Inspiration

....

What are the most important characteristics of a good friend?

_____

_____

_____

_____

_____

_____

_____

_____

_____

_____

_____

_____

_____

_____

_____

_____

_____

_____

_____

_____

_____

_____

How have you been inspired by friends or family?

_____

_____

_____

_____

_____

_____

_____

_____

_____

_____

_____

_____

_____

_____

_____

_____

_____

_____

_____

_____

_____

Inspiration

....

What is the most important thing you have learned in life?

_____

_____

_____

_____

_____

_____

_____

_____

_____

_____

_____

_____

_____

_____

_____

_____

_____

_____

_____

_____

What advice would you give future generations of your family?

_____

_____

_____

_____

_____

_____

_____

_____

_____

_____

_____

_____

_____

_____

_____

_____

_____

_____

Inspiration

Please record any other favorite memories,
stories, or messages.

_____

_____

_____

_____

_____

_____

_____

_____

_____

_____

_____

_____

_____

_____

_____

_____

_____

_____

Inspiration

WE'D LOVE TO HEAR
IF YOU HAVE ENJOYED USING
AND SHARING THIS BOOK.

————

Please send your comments to:
Book Feedback, Mail Drop 215
2501 McGee, Kansas City, Missouri 64108
or e-mail us at
booknotes@hallmark.com